Harry's Game

by Kayte Murphy
illustrated by Craig Smith

Table of Contents

Chapter 1
In Training 2

Chapter 2
Trying Hard 5

Chapter 3
Success! 12

Comprehension Check 16

Chapter 1
In Training

Harry woke up. He rolled over and groaned. Getting up early was the worst part of training for team tryouts. Starting last week, he'd been jogging every morning. He wanted to be a strong runner, just like his mom.

After school, Harry met his dad at the basketball courts. Harry's dad was a great basketball player. Harry was training for the basketball team as well as the track team!

The night before the tryouts, Harry went to bed early. He stared at his uniform. He wondered if he could ever be a track star. What if he could become a basketball superstar, too? Imaginary thoughts filled Harry's head. Which team would he really join?

Chapter 2
Trying Hard

The next morning, a sea of excited faces was waiting at the track field. Harry was quiet. He did some exercises. Then he lined up. Harry took a deep breath, and waited for the signal to start running.

Ready. Set. Go! Harry was off! Getting up for those early practices had paid off. Harry was in great shape. He ran as fast as he ever had.

After the race, the coach pulled
Harry aside.

"Good work!" she said. "I can tell
you've been training hard. You're a good
runner. But you're not quite fast enough,
yet. Come back again next year."

Harry was sad about what the coach had said. But he had to shake off his hurt. The basketball tryouts were about to begin.

Another large crowd was at the basketball courts. Harry joined a group of players. They ran up and down the court. Harry knew how to dribble and when to pass the ball.

"Great throw, Harry!" yelled the coach.

Now it was time to shoot hoops. Harry tried hard and did well. But it was hard for him to defend the basket.

The coach called him over.

"You're doing well, Harry," said the coach. "But we're looking for taller boys. I think you should try again next year."

Chapter 3
Success!

Harry left with his mom and dad.

"I'm not right for any sport," Harry sighed. "I want to go home!"

"What about soccer?" said Dad. "The tryouts are just starting over there."

"Yes!" said Mom. "Come on, Harry!"

Harry followed his parents. But he wasn't happy about another tryout.

The coach split the group into two teams. Harry was having fun. He moved the ball quickly with his feet. He ran up and down the soccer field.

At last the coach called for a break.

"This is the team," said the coach. "Charlie, John, Jess, Harry ..."

Harry could not believe it. He was on a team! Finally he had found a game that was just right for him. The best part was, Harry would be the first soccer player in his family!

Comprehension Check

Retell the Story

Use an Inference Chart and the pictures to help you retell this story.

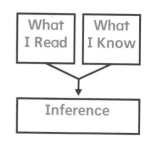

Think and Compare

1. Turn to page 10. What made you think that Harry might not make the basketball team? *(Make Inferences)*

2. Which team would you most like to play on? Why? *(Evaluate)*

3. Why do you think people like to play sports? *(Analyze)*